WINDMILLS A'
IN EAST SU⌣⌣⌣⌣⌣

The windmill is a Couris Thing
Compleatly built by art of man
To grind the corn for man and beast
That all alike may have a feast.

The mill she is built of wood, iron and stone,
Therefore she cannot go aloan;
Therefore to make the mill to go,
The wind from some part she must blow.

The motison of the mill is swift,
The miller must be very thrift
To jump about and get things ready
Or else the mill will still run empty.

Lines by a Sussex miller found by Mark Anthony Lower, 1813-1876,
affixed to a mill post – he does not say which one.

Compiled by Brigid Chapman from the research material
of the late
MAURICE LAWSON FINCH

First published in 2004 by S. B. Publications,
19 Grove Road, Seaford, East Sussex BN25 1TP
Tel: 01323 893498
E-mail: sbpublications@ tiscali.co.UK

ISBN 1 85770 293 X

Designed and typeset by CGB, Lewes. Tel 01273 476622
Printed by Fotolito Longo, Italy

CONTENTS

Front cover: Blackdown mill, Punnetts Town, Heathfield, 1980

FOREWORD

This book is compiled from material about the windmills of Sussex collected by the late Maurice Lawson Finch over some fifty years, to which he added every picture postcard showing a windmill that he could find. He was a most assiduous collector of information and there can be few references to mills in newspapers, magazines and estate agents' property sales details that escaped his eagle eye from the end of the Second World War until his death in April 2000 at the age of seventy-five.

Maurice worked initially from maps dating from 1579 to the 1900s – there is a detailed list of them in Appendix 1 – and he recorded all relevant information in respect of every mill there had been on the sites on the forms he designed for the purpose, one of which is pictured left. He completed the form in pencil, favouring H2 rather than the darker and easier-to-read HB.

With each form he filed photocopies of all published references he had obtained in respect of

PLACE	WADHURST		No	1
NAME	RIVERHALL MILL	TYPE		
EARLY REFERENCES	NO MAP REF			
DATE BUILT.				
DATE LAST IN USE.				
MOVED TO			DATE	
SEE				
DATE DEMOLISHED.	DEMOLISHED			
PRESENT CONDITION				
LAST MILLER.				
LAST OWNER.				
POSTCARDS.				
PICTURES.				
MAP REFERENCE.				
DESCRIPTIVE LOCATION & MAP.				10 E5
	7F NW OF WADHURST STA			
DATE OF LAST VISIT.				
SEE ALSO.				

4

each mill together with all correspondence relating to it; often his own site plan – for he was a skilled draughtsman – and photographs, postcards and engravings. The material covering the mills of East Susssex filled seven box files, and he amassed almost the same amount of material about the mills of West Sussex.

Maurice retired from his engineering business at Bishops Stortford in 1985 and moved with his wife, Eileen, and Simeon, the youngest of their three children, to Seaford. Previously his Sussex mill research had been confined to holiday visits to the county but he was now able to follow up every lead with visits to museums, libraries, art galleries and mill sites. He was often accompanied on his journeys of discovery by his uncle, Herbert Finch, an astronomer who moved to Hailsham in the 1940s when the Royal Observatory began its move to Herstmonceux castle. Another companion was the late Gilbert Catt, the last owner of Hamlin's smock mill at Hailsham, who retired in 1967 and later worked the watermill that had been restored by the Sussex Archaeological Society at Michelham Priory

One result of the three mill-hunters' journeys around the county is a photographic record of the many mill conversions that have taken place – usually to private houses, but with some interesting exceptions such as Hog Hill mill, Icklesham, converted in 1984 to a recording studio by its then owner, former Beatle, Paul McCartney, now Sir Paul.

Maurice planned to write a book that would add the illustrations and information he had acquired to the extensive Sussex mill archive but he did not live to do so. Eileen has, therefore, commissioned this book in his memory – and in order that the material in those seven box files is put to the use her late husband intended for it.

BRIGID CHAPMAN
LEWES
SEPTEMBER 2003

PUTTING THE WIND TO WORK

A mechanical means of harnessing the power of the wind to turn stones by which corn could be ground into meal from which bread was made was introduced to this country, possibly from Normandy, in the twelfth century. These early windmills consisted of a massive wooden post sunk into the

A medieval open trestle mill, its sweeps covered with cloth.

ground between two wooden cross trees with four supporting struts or quarter bars. They were given greater stability when the cross trees supporting the main post were mounted on brick or stone piers enclosed in a roundhouse which was used as a store.

On top of the post was the body of the mill with the sweeps attached to a wooden or metal windshaft, angled between 10 to 15 degrees to the horizontal and carrying a wooden toothed gear wheel which drove the horizontal millstones by means of a pinion. There was a wooden or metal brake band on the gear wheel so that when there was a strong wind the grinding speed of the stones could be controlled.

Sacks of grain were lifted into the mill by a hoist on the windshaft and tipped into hoppers from which it poured onto the stones. The resulting meal ran from the stones into bins or sacks, or into a dresser which separated the bran from the meal to make flour.

Access to the body of the mill was by a ladder through which protruded the tail pole that was used to turn the mill to face into the wind. It was essential that it should for if the wind blew on the back of the sweeps –

originally wooden frames covered with canvas drawn across the whole or part of each frame, depending on the wind force – they would revolve counter-clockwise with often the direst of consequences.

An improvement to the cloth or common sail was made in 1775 by Andrew Meikle. Instead of a canvas cover he filled the frame of each sail with a number of hinged shutters connected to a spring-loaded bar by which the miller could manually open or close them. Thirty years later Sir William Cubitt produced his patent sail, the shutters of which could be adjusted mechanically to provide the power required to drive the grindstones without stopping the mill.

The tower mill, as its name suggests, was a tall round or octagonal brick or stone structure with its sweeps on a cap at the top. This cap was revolved on a metal ring and the sweeps were turned head to wind by the fantail vane at the rear. There was a staging round the tower so the miller could reach the sweeps to make the necessary adjustments to the cloth covers or shutters.

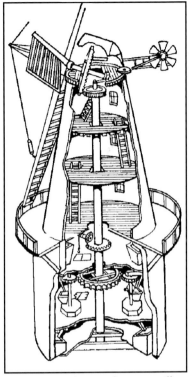

The interior layout of a tower mill.

The smock mill was a variation of the tower mill design, the octagonal body from the staging upwards being of horizontal planks of wood giving it the appearance of the smock frocks worn by workers on the land.

Building these early mills was an expensive undertaking and could only be afforded by the lord of the manor who saw to it that the villagers used the mill he had built and paid him in cash, or kind in the form of a quantity of ground corn, for the privilege. With the breaking up of the manorial system after the social catastrophe of the Black Death in the fourteenth century there was little mill building and it was not until the Industrial Revolution of the mid-eighteenth century that there were windmills in almost every town and village in Sussex. By 1813, when the first Ordnance Survey sheets covering the county were published, there were 153 sites marked on them – almost every one occupied by a working windmill.

Today, in Sussex, which was split into the administrative districts of East and West Sussex in 1888, there are five post mills, three smock mills and four tower mills still standing. Those in East Sussex are the post mills at Nutley and on Argos Hill, near Mayfield, the smock mills at Chailey and West Blatchington, near Hove, and the tower mills at Polegate and Stone Cross.

They are open to view on National Mills Day, usually the second Sunday in May, and on Sundays and perhaps a weekday from April to September. The Sussex Mills Group, formed to promote the study and restoration of mills, issues a leaflet giving full details of the individual mills and theiropening times. It is available from the secretary, D H Cox, 3 Middle Road, Partridge Green, Horsham, West Susssex RH 13 8JA. Tel: 01403 711137

The tower mill in 1980 – as part of Mill House on West Bank.
Photo: MLF

Alfriston

This much-visited village was a centre for local trade from the mid-eighteenth century and a tithe map of 1843 shows it had two windmills – a post mill 190 metres west north west of the Market Cross and a tower mill on West Bank to the south of the village. The post mill, which was insured for £300 on a Royal Exchange Fire Insurance Policy in February 1791 when it was owned by John French, was dismantled in 1908 by millwright Luther Pearce. He was assisted by Dicker miller Ephraim Ovenden, and a pair of the post mill's sweeps were added to Dicker new mill.

The four double-shuttered sweeps of the tower mill, built in 1835 opposite Dean's Place House (TQ 518027), had barely begun to turn when they were damaged by the storm force winds that swept across Sussex on 29 November 1836. They were quickly repaired and the mill continued to grind corn until 1905 when a sweep struck a passing cow with fatal results to both. The site was sold and the lease surrendered two years later by George Hewett of Lullington Court Farm, who had held it since 1881. Among the millers who worked it for him was Joseph Fearse, nicknamed 'Nosey' not for any physical abnormality or inquisitiveness but because he often went about the village with a protective leather mask over his nose. The poor man suffered from asthma, as did so many millers in the later years of their lives, from the inhalation of flour dust.

The tower mill was converted to a private house in 1910. It was on the market, 'with spacious and unusual accommodation', in 1994 at an asking price of £225,000.

× B ×

CIRCULAR ROUTE VIA SILVERHILL *is on the destination board of the trolley bus shown passing Baldslow mill on this postcard from the days when the inland postage rate was a half penny.*

Baldslow

The post mill on The Ridge above Hastings, to the south east of this little village and shown on the 1813 OS map, was replaced by a more modern smock mill some fifty years later. It is the octagonal base of this second mill that now forms a large part of the private house that has been on this site (TQ 801132) since the 1930s.

The old mill had stairs on the outside and these had to be raised by a lever whenever the miller, John Hayward, needed to turn the mill to face the wind. When he died in 1846 he left it to his nephew, another John Hayward, who replaced the old mill in 1856

The converted mill, 'fully modernised with many unusual features', when it was for sale in the 1950s.

11

with a smock mill built by millwrights Upfields of Catsfield. It had five floors, and an automatic cap and a fan at the rear which moved it to face the wind. This mill, known locally as the Harrow Mill after an inn of that name in the village, worked under wind power until it lost its sweeps in a gale in the First World War and was converted to steam. A decade or so later it was bought by Mr F Richmond, the owner of the adjoining land. He removed the cap, cut off the top two floors and turned it into a private house.

❏ ❏ ❏

Battle

Only one of the mill sites shown on earlier maps of this capital of 1066 Country still has a windmill upon it. The post mill built c1724 on Caldbec Hill (TQ 746166) was replaced some time after 1795 with a smock mill that ceased working in 1924 and was converted and extended to form a private house. In its new role it retained its fantail, cap and the centre spars of its four sweeps certainly until 1973 when it featured, with a photograph, in an article about watermills and windmills as homes in the property section of *The Times*. It has since lost the spars of its sails but its Derbyshire Peak and

The mill on Caldbec Hill is shown as part of a fine country house on this card published by Barrett of Battle.

French burr millstones have been set in the ground outside the front door and on the patio.

Telham post mill, also known as Black Horse mill, stood on the east side of the A2100 to Hastings (TQ 766149). It ceased producing WALLIS'S NOTED HIGH CLASS BREAD AND FLOUR in 1937 and was demolished in 1962. For a time after the Second World War the cottage beside it was used as a tea room, the derelict mill in the background proving an attraction to customers.

❐ ❐ ❐

Berwick

The history of the mill that bore the name of this village, noted for the wall paintings in its church by Bloomsbury Group artists Duncan Grant, Vanessa Bell and her son Quentin Bell, can be traced from advertisements and news stories that appeared in the *Sussex Weekly Advertiser.*

On 4 May 1778 the sale by private treaty was announced of 'all that good-accustomed well-winded Wind Mill, the same being in good repair, standing in the parish of Alfriston. . . .' Two years later the mill 'together with almost a new cart and two good horses', was to be sold by auction on 15 May. However, on 8 May 1780 readers were told that it had been sold by private contract and only the cart and horses would be sold at auction.

Then the private buyer defaulted, 'paid a fine to be off from his Bargain' and the mill, together with the cart and horses, went under the hammer at the Star, Alfriston on 1 June and was bought by John Ade.

The newspaper, on 15 May 1881, reported the mill's dramatic end:

> During a violent gale from the south west which prevailed on Monday last (May 7) the Berwick windmill, which has stood for centuries, has fallen by fire caused, it is presumed, by friction of the brake. The flaming sails, uncontrolled by the brake, revolved with great rapidity like a great Catherine Wheel . . .

❐ ❐ ❐

Bexhill

The high ground to the north of this seaside resort developed by Lord de la Warr in 1885 to the south of the old village and its Saxon church was once dotted with windmills. The last to go was a post mill, built c1780 and known as the Down or Hoad's Mill (TQ 733087). It was owned by the Hoad family from 1857 and for years they ground special sheaves of corn

Down or Hoad's post mill c1928

for the communion wafers used at the harvest festival service at St Mark's church, Little Common.

In 1930 the mill was working 'in conjunction with a modern electric bakery' but in 1955 its then owner, Clifford Hoad, was trying to give it away to save it from destruction. He told the *Sussex Daily News* that he could no longer afford to keep it in repair, that the county council's planning committee had decided 'with regret' that it could not contribute to the cost of renovation, and that he hoped some public body would take it away and put it up somewhere else in the borough.

No one took him up on his offer and the following year one of the 30ft sweeps came crashing down in a gale. Bits continued to fall off the mill until 1965 when the whole structure collapsed leaving only part of the base above ground. Some remains of the centre post and roundhouse are still there today, on the west side of Gunter's Lane and surrounded by the houses of Glenleigh Park.

A mill that was sold and taken to Kent was Pankhurst's smock mill at Sidley, built c1798. In 1928 Mr W A Tomlinson, whose son, Reginald, was at school in Sevenoaks with Maurice Lawson Finch, bought it for £25 from the last miller, Douglas Pankhurst, and had it hauled by a traction engine to

Stocks Green at Leigh where it was re-erected and restored at a cost of £1,500. There it stood, beside the oast house of his Old Barn Tea Rooms, until it collapsed in 1963.

❒ ❒ ❒

Bishopstone

One of the earliest windmill sites in Sussex was in this settlement to the east of Newhaven harbour and later on it had the largest watermill, or rather tidemill, ever constructed in the county. The windmill belonged to 'Pagan, the clerk, of good memory' and in 1189 it was bought from his heir by Bishop Seffrid II for five marks (£6.33p). He left it in trust to the

canons of Chichester cathedral to pay for a Mass to be said for his soul on the anniversary of his death.

On old pictures of the tidemills, like the one on the right, the sweeps of a smock mill can be seen behind the main building on the site. This windmill was not used to grind corn but to power the hoist used for loading and unloading the barges that came up the tidal channel to the wharf.

❏ ❏ ❏

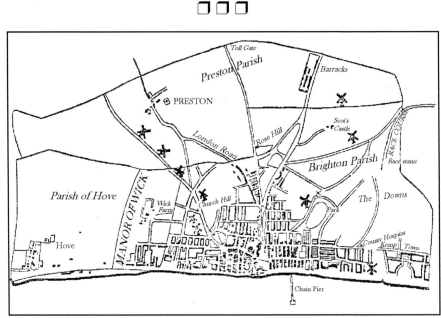

The windmills of Brighton that were shown on the 1813 Ordnance Survey map.

Brighton

It is difficult to be exact about the age, location and type of the windmills in this fishing village that became a royal resort in the late eighteenth century and is now a vibrant city of the twenty-first century because of the number of windmills involved, the vagueness of the information available about them and the fact that at least four were moved from their original sites.

More than thirty windmill sites are shown within the boundaries of Brighton and Hove on maps from Saxton's of 1579 to the Volunteer Review map of 1862. All but two have gone. The rest fell down, were demolished, burnt down, blown down or moved away to West Sussex before the First World War.

West Blatchington smock mill. Photo: MLF 1982

One that has survived and can be visited is in Holmes Avenue, West Blatchington (TQ 279068). It is a smock mill that was built *c*1820 on a square brick and flint base in the centre of a complex of barns, only one of which now remains. The mill, which John Constable painted in 1825, four years before he was elected a Royal Academician, ceased working in 1897 when its sweeps were blown off in a gale. It was bought by Hove Borough Council in 1937 and has since been restored to a standard that gained the mill a Civic Trust Commendation in 1988. The original machinery is back in working order and it occasionally grinds corn.

The other mill that survived is Patcham or Waterhall tower mill, high on the Downs between the A23 and the road to the Devil's Dyke (TQ 303084). It was built by Joseph Harris in 1885 on the site of a much earlier mill. When he finished his apprenticeship at Ballards old bonnet mill, also at Patcham, Harris set up as a baker in premises in Old London Road and, after a few years, decided to build a steam mill beside his shop. He was refused permission so instead he built one of the last windmills to go up in Sussex, if not in England, at a cost of around £1,000.

Patcham mill ceased working in 1922 and, after the Second World War, when it was used as a lookout post by the Home Guard, it was for a time a tea house run by two sisters. Brighton Council objected to this change of use, the sisters appealed and the Minister of Housing and Local Government, Harold Macmillan, decided in their favour. On 12 January 1954 the Daily Express announced:

Greetings   Patcham Mill   PATCHAM
from   Tea House   BRIGHTON
                                   Tel: 54857

The windmill sisters can serve tea

and the same story was carried by the *Daily Mail* with the headline: 'The Minister allows a cup of tea'.

The mill was converted to a private house in the 1960s and has since been extended and improved by successive owners. It was on the market in 1999 with a price tag of £1.2 million.

The first of the four mills that were moved was the West mill, which belonged to Mr Streeter. On 29 March 1797 the framework of this post mill was mounted on runners attached to a timber stay and hauled by eighty four oxen harnessed in six teams, with two beasts in

Patcham or Waterhall mill in 1999 as a private house

A mill on the move. Miller Thomas Hodson was in charge of the six teams of oxen that hauled the West mill from near Regency Square to the top of Dyke Road in 1757.

reserve, the two miles from a site near Regency Square to one in Dyke Road overlooking the village of Preston. The mill originally stood near the former Bedford Hotel in Belle Vue Gardens and a new site had to be found for it as a result of complaints by owners of adjoining properties who wanted the area to expand residentially rather than commercially. It was taken to the top of what is now Miller's Road and placed to the south of the Dyke Road Hotel.

Next to be moved was one of the two post mills in Clifton Gardens. It was taken the short distance to Windmill Street *c*1835 and there it was joined in the 1830s by Taylor's mill, also known as East End mill, which formerly stood in a field that later became Sudeley Place, to the west of Kemp Town. This post mill was moved again in 1862 – to the Race Hill where it was a landmark for racegoers

The mill on the Race Hill, c1896. Photo: SCM

until it was blown down on 16 May, 1913. Not far away from it, to the west, was Bear Mill and below that, off Elm Grove, was Hanover Mill.

There is some confusion about from which of the mill sites on the east side of Dyke Road in 1847 came the white smock mill that was moved to West Sussex in 1851 to become 'Jill' of the famous 'Jack and Jill' mills standing today on Clayton Hill. There is little doubt that the mill bought in 1847 by James Mitchell of Clayton Court Farm was the white post mill built for Henry Lashmar in 1821 for that date, '1821', is carved inside 'Jill'. But did it come from the Port Hall site that was occupied by Lashmar's Old Mill from 1800 or was it the one that been moved to higher ground above the tunnel in Belmont Road to replace Murrell's Old Mill which stood there in 1813?

A mill that stayed on the site on which it was built (TQ 316057) from 1838 until it was demolished in 1913, was the tower mill off Ditchling Road. It was built for John Ingleden, a baker of 18 St James Street,

Cuttress's mill and shop.

Brighton and bought in 1880 by Charles Cuttress, a Ditchling miller and founder of the bakery and catering business, Forfars. He and his son, who sold the bread and cakes they made in their shop adjoining the mill, worked it by wind power until the end of the century when the sweeps were made fast and a steam engine installed to operate the grinding mechanism.

Brighton builder William Daws bought the mill in 1912 for £325, knocked it down and used its bricks and timbers for the houses he was building in what is now Belton Road.

A mill with links to a murder that had the whole town talking in the mid-nineteenth century was Hodson's black mill, a sturdy twelve-sided smock mill which stood 100 yards to the east of the Clifton Road Congregational church from 1804 until it was demolished in 1866. It was worked by the Hodson family and one summer's evening in 1849 Charles Hodson and his brother were driving back to Brighton, having dined with friends near Henfield, when they came across a body of a man lying in the road a mile from the Dale turnpike gate at Newtimber.. They got out of their trap and discovered it was someone they knew well – John Stonehouse Griffith,

the owner of the Rock Brewery in St James Street – and he had a pistol by his side. The question of suicide was raised at the inquest but when it was shown that the pistol had not been fired since it was last cleaned a verdict of wilful murder was returned.

William Vine's mill in 1843 from a painting by Henry Bodle.
Photo: SCM

In the case of Vine's mill on a site in what is now Vine Place on the west side of Dyke Road, (TQ 306047), it was the miller, rather than the mill, that moved from place to place.

William Vine came from Windoor mill on the Downs between Lullington and Wilmington to Ballards old bonnet mill at Patcham in 1813 and spent five years there before moving to the post mill that bore his name. He was an introspective, pious man, a devout member of Salem Chapel in Bond Street, Brighton, and much given to expressing himself in verse. William died in 1837, his mill passed into other hands and was demolished. He described his new home in these words:

William Vine on the Church Hill
Just by the side of a wind mill;
The dwelling's neat and fenced around,
Its inmates dwell on mercy's Ground.

21

Burwash

On the south side of the A265, along the road to Heathfield, (TQ 631232) was Rockhill post mill which was worked by Samuel Dallaway, succeeded by his three sons, until 1923. It was standing derelict and without its sweeps, surrounded by a Mill House poultry farm in 1937, but had gone by

1979 when Arthur Smith did his survey of Sussex windmills. The windmill weathervane, pictured left, was on Mill House until the storm of October 1987. It depicts a tower mill, not a post mill – perhaps the one on Copper's Hill, further to the east along the A265 (TQ 664241).

On a summer's day in 1797 a little girl had a narrow escape from death or serious injury when she inadvertently went for a ride on one of the sweeps of the tower mill on Copper Hill. The *Sussex Weekly Advertiser* of 5 August carried the story.

The girl, 'named Langridge' was 'at play near Mr Hilder's windmill when she was taken up by one of the swifts and carried round till in its revolution she came again to the ground, where she extracted herself and was by the man rescued, unhurt.'

The child had been lifted to a height of 63ft and dropped 6ft to the ground as the sweep completed its revolution.

Chailey

The exact centre of Sussex is marked in this large parish by a handsome white smock mill, now housing a museum of agricultural implements and rural bygones. The mill on North Common (TQ 387214) has had a chequered history. It was built on a site at West Hoathly c1830, dismantled fourteen years later and carted the twenty or so miles to Newhaven where it worked until 1864. It was then taken down and brought to Chailey to replace a collapsing post mill. It ceased working in 1911 and its cap and sweeps blew off in 1928. They were replaced and blew off again in 1935.

For a time from April 1954, when it was officially opened by Lord Rowallan, the Chief Scout, the North Common mill served as the head-quarters of the 2nd Chailey

The mill on North Common, Chailey in 1936.

(Heritage) Scout Group but it gradually became more and more derelict. In 1985 the parish council moved in to save it and three years and £20,000 later the village and Friends of Chailey Windmill had a tourist attraction to be proud of. A lottery grant of £43,000 received in 1996 has financed further improvements and the mill is open on National Mills Day and on Sunday afternoons from April to September.

The remains of the base of South Common smock mill in a field off Mill Lane.
Photo: MLF 1986

A white smock mill was brought from Yokehurst Wood to South Common , South Chailey in 1809. It had been advertised for sale in the *Sussex Weekly Advertiser* in September of the previous year as 'a good timbered smock mill . . . to be removed before next May.' By the early 1900s most of its machinery had gone and it was being used as a store.

❏ ❏ ❏

Chiddingly

THE mill on this GREETINGS FROM CHIDDINGLY postcard, franked 7 July 1916, was to the south of The Dicker, now the A22, at Golden Cross. It was

the last of a number of mills that had been on the site (TQ 537123) and was built c1823 by the Lewes mill-wrights, Samuel and William Medhurst.

It had a Sussex tailpole fan, a device the Medhurst brothers were said

Golden Cross post mill and, right, the turned-by-hand Dicker new mill..

to have invented to turn the sails of a post mill into the wind. Without it the miller had the backbreaking job of turning the mill on its trestle by hand. Golden Cross mill ceased working in 1915 and its base was incorporated into a private house named The Old Mill.

Another mill in this large parish was at Lower Dicker. It was built in 1805 by a group of farmers to grind their corn and was variously called Dicker new mill, Ovenden's mill and Hide's mill as the tenancy changed hands over the years. It was a white post mill on three floors above a large black tarred brick roundhouse and was kept well up to date by its owners. In the early 1900s Benjamin Hide tried auxiliary power in the form of a steam engine set up in a shed some distance away to turn the burr stones that came from Bishopstone Tidemills. This experiment was not a success and the mill had reverted to wind power when its centre post snapped in a gale and it came crashing down on 29 December 1929.

❏ ❏ ❏

Cross in Hand

There is no written record to confirm the arcane tradition that *Cruce*

The roundhouse of the old post mill at Cross in Hand with the new mill on the right.
Photo: MLF
1985

Manus – or Cross in Hand – was where Crusader knights assembled with their esquires and men-at-arms on their way to the coast to take ship to the Holy Land. However, much has been written about the white post mill, believed to be the largest in the county with a post 2ft 6ins square, which was brought here from Mount Ephraim, south of Uckfield, in 1855 by miller William Kenward. It stands on a bank (TQ 558218) on the north side of the Cross in Hand to Lewes turnpike, now the B2102, about half a mile from its junction with the A267. Some 100 yards from it is the roundhouse of Cross in Hand's old mill, which ceased working in 1903.

The new mill was first sited on the opposite side of the road about a quarter of a mile further south. Its presence there did not please art collector Louis Huth, the owner of Possingworth Park. He had spent £60,000 on the neo-Gothic mansion, and the park that surrounded it, so he could entertain his London friends in privacy. A windmill clacking away on the skyline was not what he wanted so it had to be moved. With the aid of rollers and a team of oxen the mill was hauled to its present site in 1868 and continued to grind barley, oats and maize until 1969 when a stock broke while the sweeps were turning in the wind.

A similar accident had occurred in October 1932 and the miller, Sidney Ashdown, wrote a letter to his friend, Gilbert Catt, at Hamlin's Mill, Hailsham, telling him all about it. In the envelope, on which was a 1fid stamp bearing the head of King George V (1910-1936) and franked 23 OC 3--. he enclosed the postcard on the facing page, which is captioned: 'THE DAMAGED WINDMILL. CROSS-IN-HAND. OCT 1932'.

The letter, from the Mill House, Cross in Hand and dated 22/10/32, reads:

Dear Gilbert

I do not know if you recognise this windmill post card. Well this happened yesterday Friday at about 4.30pm. The old mill was running very well with one pair, oat 'grinding', when the inner 'stock' broke asunder [and] the best two sweeps were broken.

Nobody was with her at the time and she did not hurt anyone at all. We were unable to get near to her for a time for wood was flying everywhere. At last she was made safe.

We shall have to run with 2 sweeps for a time.

No serious damage was done inside, only two cogs broken out of the brake wheel.

Yours sincerely
Sidney Ashdown.

Printers were quickly off the mark when any newsworthy disasters occurred in their locality and, if a photograph of it was available, they would have postcards out in next to no time.

'Certainly it is not beyond the bounds of possibility for a photograph to have been taken of the damaged mill early on the morning of 22 October, developed from the glass plate, and copies run off on a flat bed press and be in shops in the area as postcards by midday', said Steve Benz, founder of S. B. Publications and secretary of the East Susssex Postcard Club.

The only niggling query is how could Gilbert Catt be expected to recognise the 'windmill postcard' unless, of course, Sidney meant the 'windmill on the postcard'.

After this accident the mill worked with two sweeps until a new pair was fitted in the 1950s. They had only been in place for a few years when – on Friday, 13 November 1959 – the mill was struck by lightning. One of the sweeps snapped off and about £400 worth of damage was done to the structure. Then, in June 1969, only a few days after the mill was back in working order once again, another stock broke and that was the end of its working life.

A certain amount of repair and restoration work was carried out by the owners, Mr and Mrs Jack Newnham, and for a time it looked as if the county council would come up with some cash. Inflation, and other financial crises in the 1980s, put paid to that idea and the mill, although still standing, is in a derelict condition. Its history has been neatly encapsulated in this poem by Mary Ashdown, whose husband, Jack, is the brother of Sidney:

T'was first in 1855 it came,
From the site at Mount Ephraim.
Near Possingworth first it did stand
When it came to Cross-in-Hand.

Then in 1868 it left its place
Though now two 'swips' are off its face
On the hill it stands proud and grand
To grind the best corn in the land.

The poor old mill was once so white.
So that it could not be seen at night,
It was sprayed as green as any grass
To fool the Huns as they did pass.

It is the last of Sussex mills
To turn its sails o'er the hills.
Many years I hope 'twill stand
Upon the hill at Cross-in-Hand.

Pratt's mill, Crowborough, on a card posted on 19 July 1908.

Crowborough

The tower mill, built on Crowbough Hill (TQ 518310) by Baptist minister, Richard Pratt, in 1862 was the scene of a tragic accident the following year. His eighteen year-old son, Jesse, was killed when his clothing was caught in the machinery and he was crushed against the upright shaft.

The mill last worked in 1922, but it was then powered by a gas engine rather than by the wind. Two years later it was bought, together with the old shop beside it, by a local builder, Mr A J Holcombe. He took off the top of the tower and used its bricks and timbers to convert the

Pratt's tower mill converted to a house. Photo: MLF 1982

mill and the shop to a house for his own occupation.

The fire that was lit on Beacon Hill in 1588 was part of a chain that warned the people of England of the presence of the Spanish Armada in the English Channel.

The hill, 800ft above sea level, was a mill site from 1795. The last mill to stand on it is pictured, left, on a card dated 1904. It is without its sweeps and topped by a turreted superstructure with a beacon basket on one corner and a weathervane on another.

By the 1980s that had all gone and on the site in Mill Lane, off Beacon Road, (TQ 513309) were a few stones from the base of the roundhouse and a rusty water tank with graffiti announcing 'Andy is Gay'.

⌐ ⌐ ⌐

Onlookers inspecting Dallington mill after it had been pulled down in 1913.
Photo: G A Catt.

Dallington

The white wooden smock mill on a two storey brick base, built *c*1851 in a field about 200 yards north east of the church, was demolished in 1913. It had been offered for sale in the *Sussex Weekly Advertiser* of 2 August 1881 when it was 'in good order, built of the best materials . . . fitted with a grain cracking mill, the usual machinery and has patent sweeps plus brick and tile stables for three horses and a van lodge.' The mill did not disappear totally. The base was used as a store up to the Second World War and part of it was still standing in the field behind the church in 1980.

□ □ □

Denton

The storm that hit Sussex on 8 January 1734-35 'began to blow pretty strong about 9 or 10 in the morning and continued to increase until about 12 o'clock, when there was all of a sudden such a hurricane as blew down an abundance of barns, windmills and trees by the roots' wrote Edward Boys, rent collector for the Gage family of Firle. One of the mills was at Denton but it was repaired or rebuilt because it appears on a map of 1779.

The Round House at Splash Point on a card postmarked 1910.

Eastbourne

The roundhouse of a windmill on the beach close to where the pier now stands became a royal holiday home in July 1780 when King George III and Queen Charlotte sent four of their younger children to this rich agricultural parish. Twelve year old Prince Edward, who became Duke of Kent and father of Queen Victoria, stayed with his tutors at the Round House which had been converted into 'very commodious apartments' by James Gandon after the mill had lost its sweeps in a storm some ten years previously.

The sweeps were the most unusual part of this mill for they were mounted on top rather than at the side of the structure and turned horizontally instead of vertically. The mill was built by Eastbourne corn merchant and Customs House Officer Thomas Mortimer and he followed it, in 1752, with another one on Pashley Down, the site of which (TQ 593982) was excavated in the 1960s by Lawrence and Patricia Stevens and Richard

Gilbert with teams of boys from Eastbourne College and Eastbourne Grammar School.

They uncovered the foundations of an early sixteenth century post mill and Mortimer's horizontal mill with a bolting house beside it, together with pottery fragments, glazed brickwork and glass. An illustrated account of these excavations, by Lawrence Stevens, is in volume 120 of the *Sussex Archaeological Collections*.

Mortimer's mill was burnt down on 3 April 1811 and a year or so later a three-floored white tower mill, known as Ocklynge mill, was built on a site to the south (TQ 595007). It ceased work in 1894, became increasingly derelict, and was blown up with dynamite in the 1930s to make way for new housing in

Ocklynge mill in 1925

Windmill Close to the west of the A22 Willingdon Road.

One of Eastbourne's oldest mill sites, where Watts Lane joins Mill Road, belonged to the manor of St John of Jerusalem in the Middle Ages. On it, from 1724, was the Rectory mill, also known as the White mill to distinguish it from Gildredge Manor's black post mill which stood nearby. The White mill was advertised for sale in January 1885, 'at a bargain price as it must be removed' because the land was needed for housing. It was eventually bought for £15 by Ocklynge miller Edgar Baker, who demolished it with the help of Samuel Dallaway who took its cap on a trolley to the mill he had built at Stone Cross for use as a grain store. The neighbouring black mill was demolished by developer George Boulton in 1878 after it failed to get a bid at auction.

The last of Eastbourne's mills to go was from near this site (TQ

33

599001). It was the tower mill built by William Hurst in 1808. It survived being struck by lightning in January 1884 although 'the interior had been so much injured that £100 would hardly cover the loss' and the miller, Edward Hurst, who was in his office near the mill 'was rendered momentarily unconscious'.

The mill continued working until 1917 when part of the machinery of the cap jammed. It was then powered for a time by steam and a sign near the mill advertised Hurst's Steam Flour Mills and Bread Factory. In 1948 it was partially demolished, the base of the mill being used as a store by the building firm of Y L Lovell. It was finally removed in 1979 to provide parking space for the firm's vans . . .

❏ ❏ ❏

East Grinstead

North End post mill c1900

There were only two windmills in this town on the Surrey/Kent borders and the *Susssex Weekly Advertiser*, in reporting the great gale of November 1773, does not say which one had 'the top of its round beam twisted fairly off and was blown to the ground and shivered to pieces'.

The post mill that replaced the one on East Grinstead Common that was burnt down in 1757 was known as North End mill. It was demolished in the early 1900s and on its site (TQ 386391) today are the houses, schools and business premises of Windmill Lane, which branches to the right off the A22 London Road past St Mary's church.

There is also a Windmill Lane branching right off the A22 just before it reaches Ashurst Wood. Here (TQ417370) stood Cutten's smock mill, which was pulled down in 1882.

What East Grinstead lacked in the way of windmills it made up for with watermills. It had seven on the headwaters of the Medway, which rises at Turner's Hill, and several more on the tributaries of the Wey on the border with Surrey and Kent. Some ground corn but the majority provided power for the foundries of the iron industry which flourished in this area until the early nineteenth century.

Cutten's smock mill. Photo SCM.

❏ ❑ ❏

Fairlight

The cliffs here are, at 599ft above sea level, the highest on this part of the coast and Victorian holidaymakers came in their hundreds to admire the view of the 'ten towns, two harbours, three bays, sixty-six churches, five castles, seven Martello towers, one lighthouse and forty windmills . . .' that the Reverend T W Horsfield mentions in his *Antiquities of Sussex.*

Such an excursion in 1830 proved fatal for Sir Frederick Baker, a baronet from Devonshire who was visiting Fairlight Down with his family. The *Annual Register* reported that, 'being shortsighted', he approached too near the smock mill on Fairlight Down, was struck by one of its sweeps on the back of the head 'and shortly after breathed his last'.

The mill site – the most easterly of the four on the West Hill above Hastings – is shown on maps from 1724 and the smock mill, which had a conical cap, was built there in 1819. It burnt down in 1869 together with three adjoining granaries in one of which an old man who had a souvenir stall on the cliffs kept his stock in trade,which included a telescope worth £4.

Another mill in the locality that burnt down was at Bachelor's Bump, a hill to the north east of the A259. It had been moved from Ewhurst, where it was known as Brasses mill, sometime after 1823. It lost two sweeps in a storm in 1856 and on 21 April two years later the machinery overheated and caught fire.

Firle

Archaeologists who excavated what they thought was an ancient earthwork on Firle Beacon in 1913 announced to the world that they had found the remains of a sidereal clock. However, what they had found was the vestigial remains of the mill or mills that stood on the site shown on maps from pre-Armada days to 1783.

Flimwell mill being demolished in 1893 – from the collection of Miss Minnie Barfoot of Mount Cottage, Hawkhurst Road.

Flimwell

The mill site (TQ 717312) on the Mount, a hill 464ft above sea level a few hundred yards south of the Kent county boundary and to the east of the A21 to Hastings, is shown of maps from 1724. The post mill that occupied it from 1805 was demolished in 1893 and it took twelve horses to pull the mill down – and the villagers turned out in force to help. One of its Derbyshire Peak millstones was set in the ground outside the gate of Mount Cottage on the A268Hawkhurst Road and it was still there in 1981.

❏ ❏ ❏

Framfield

It must have been hard work for the teams of horses that hauled a post mill, built in 1808 by Edward Elphick at Glynde, the six or so miles to the parish of Framfield in 1868. They accomplished the feat, without incident, and the mill on its new site, south of the B2102 road to Blackboys,(TQ 520206) continued working by wind

Blackboys recreation ground – and its windmill

power well into the 1930s. Because of its position it was called Blackboys mill and, as the years passed, it became more part of that village than of Framfield. When it ceased working it became increasingly derelict and although Uckfield Rural District Council put a protection order on it in 1938 this did not prevent it being demolished after the Second World War.

❏ ❏ ❏

Friston

The mills that stood successively on top of a hill (TQ 552983) between the coast road to Eastbourne (now the A259) and the old road to Willingdon were all either burnt down, blown down or fell down. First to go, 'between four and five o'clock on 14 February 1761' according to the *Sussex Weekly Advertiser*, was the post mill belonging to George Medley of Buxted Place. It was burnt down and three soldiers 'were taken up on suspicion of setting fire to it.'

The mill was replaced, but its successor was struck by lightning on 12 February 1769 and finally blown down on 26 March fifty-seven years later. The grinder and his mate were fortunately able to get clear before it fell over.

Friston's third windmill was a four-sail post mill without a fan but with

Friston mill with the pond in the foreground, c1920.

a tailpole, built in 1826 for Colonel Maitland of Friston Place. The last miller, from 1890 until he died in 1922, was William George Morris. He was also the sexton and a chorister of St Mary's church, on the seaward side of the coast road. The mill collapsed on a calm day in January 1926. The centre post, crown beam and part of the roundhouse remained standing until the site was cleared in 1933 to make way for the houses of Windmill Close.

❏ ❏ ❏

Glynde

The earliest mention of a mill at Glynde is in the Archbishop of Canterbury's custumals of the Manor of South Malling which refer, in 1285, to 'Roger atte Wyke miller', the settlement of Wyke being south west of Week Lane (TQ 446106) on the Glynde parish boundary with Ringmer.

It was the discovery of three pieces of French burr millstone when four barrows were being investigated on Glynde Hill (TQ 447096) in the 1980s that revealed the site of the mill referred to in a lease of 1576 which restricted Brigden Farm's sheep pasture on Caburn Hill 'to the foteparth that ledith from Glynd to Lewes upon the down between the wyndmyll and Calbroughhill'.

The post mill that was moved to Blackboys Corner in the parish of Framfield in 1868 was the one built by Edward Elphick 'at his own expense . . . on eight perches more or less situate in Beddingham' (TQ 460085), that he had leased from Viscount Hampden and his brother, John Trevor, for a period of sixty years from 1 February 1808. Elphick died in 1824 and the windmill was acquired, together with the miller's house and other buildings, by the Glynde Estate for £965.5s in 1839. It was bought twenty-eight years later for £80 by Heathfield farmer, Edward Hobden, for his son, John, a master miller of Framfield.

Buried in bushes near the railway station at Glynde (TQ 457087) are the remains of a hollow post mill. It drove two lifting pumps that supplied water for the steam engine that powered the Telpherage Company's mile long aerial electric railway that brought containers loaded with gault clay from the pit near Decoy Wood down to trucks on the railway sidings which would take it to the Sussex Portland Cement Works at South Heighton. This aerial railway was opened on 17 October 1885 but by 1889 it had been replaced by a tramway.

Guestling

The smock mill that stood at the top of Mill Lane, (TQ 861155) three quarters of a mile to the north east of the Church St Laurence, was pulled down or fell down some time before the First World War.

It was a replacement for the open-trestle post mill, pictured left, that was shown on the site on maps from 1724 to 1815.

As can be seen from the drawing by S J Heady, taken from a watercolour by an un-named artist, and dated 1827, the mill had lost its sweeps and was in an extremely dilapidated state.

❐ ❐ ❐

Hailsham

The Lower mill was built by Hubbard, a millwright of Lewes, for a Mr Kenwood in 1834 and burnt down in 1923, by which time its name had been changed to Hamlin's mill. This smock mill, which had a domed cap and a fan with a chain hanging down to move the patent sails, stood in what

is now Mill Road (TQ 598089). It was originally fitted with a pair of wheat stones for grinding hog corn, and another pair of wheat stones were added later.

Hamlin's mill changed hands ten times before becoming the property of David Catt who, as a young man, was employed at the mill at Cowbeech which was destroyed by lightning in 1905. He worked it in partnership with a Mr Dann, who looked after the accounts, and Mr Boniface who worked as the loader, from 1879 when the miller, John Mercer, wrote to his customers informing them that he was relinquishing the mill in favour of 'Messrs Dann, Catt and Boniface' who he strongly recommended for their 'business abilities, honesty and sobriety'.

Hamlin's smock mill.
Photo: G A Catt.

Seven years later David Catt bought out his partners and carried on the business alone. The balance sheet for that year shows that his total outgoings were £348 11s, his income from sales of wheat, oats and '280 bags of flour at 6s a bag', was £379 and he made a profit of £30. 9s. He was paying £50 mortgage interest; his wage bill, including his own £52 10s a year, was £176. 2s; the keep for horses and a pony was £63; and rates and taxes amounted to £15 15s. 0d. David

Catt died in 1924 and was succeeded in the business by his son Ebenezer and grandsons Gilbert, Jack and Hector.

The Upper mill, a post mill built in 1789 and later known as Harebeating mill, was originally on St Wilfrid's Green at the top of the High Street. While it was there one of the millers was dragged to his death when the smock frock he was wearing was caught up in the gearing.

The mill was moved in the latter part of the nineteenth century to a site on Harebeating Lane (TQ 592097) and ceased working around 1915. In the 1980s the round house, pictured left, with the post and crown beam on top, made an unusual feature in the garden behind Mill House in Harebeating Lane.

◻ ◻ ◻

Draper's fine smock mill in 1934.

Hastings

Ten windmill sites are mapped on the hills around Hastings and the mills that stood on them are described in *Historic Hastings* by J Manwaring Baines, curator of Hastings museum from 1935 to 1972.

The last to go was Draper's mill on Silverhill in St Leonards. It was the third mill on this site (TQ 797105),off Sedlescombe Road South overlooking the marshy lands of Bulverhythe and it ceased working in 1941 when its sweeps were secured facing into the prevailing wind and the shutters removed. Efforts were made in the 1950s to preserve this smock mill but

This undated and unidentified card, showing two of the West Hill mills, was bought by MLF from an antiques fair at Ardingly.

the borough council found the £3,000 estimated cost of the restoration work needing to be done prohibitive and it was demolished in the early 1960s.

There were five mills on the West Hill – four ran in a line to the north of the road to Ore and the fifth was French's mill, built for £300 at the junction of Priory Street and Croft Road in 1808. Specifications for this mill, the site of which disappeared from maps after 1835, are given in John French's contract with Robertsbridge millwright, Cornelius Wetherell, which is now in Hastings museum. The outside diameter of the brick base was to be 18ft and the overall height 40ft with 'bottom, middle and top floors'. The stocks of the sweeps were to be of fir, 36ft long and 11ins by 8ins wide, and the sail rods, 'of the same material', 8ins by 5ins and the 'Round Beam of Oak' 2ft, tapering to 1ft 3ins.

At Hastings, as at Brighton and other coastal towns, there was a building boom in the early years of the nineteenth century to cater for the increasing seaside holiday trade. Windmills that were in the way had to go, not only to make room for houses but to comply with regulations introduced in the reign of William IV requiring them to be screened from traffic using any turnpike road to prevent them frightening the horses.

Windmills around Heathfield – from a 1910 map of the parish.

Heathfield

The mills around this market town ground the oats for the chicken fattening industry which in the 1930s was dealing with a million birds a year – representing a cash crop of £500,000. It was at Cade Street in the 1780s that cramming chickens with a mixture of milk, fat and dried oats was first developed commercially. They would arrive from Surrey lean and alive and, after four weeks of machine feeding, leave fat, dead and dusted with flour.

Six of these windmills were still standing in 1910 when Perceval Lucas prepared the map from which the one on the facing page is based. Others, like the post mills at Cade Street and Broad Oak had long gone.

It is as a result of the dedication of Archie Dallaway to the windmill that his great-grandfather had brought in 1856 by teams of horses and oxen from Biddenden in Kent that it is still standing in good order on Blackdown Hill (TQ 627209) at Punnetts Town.

Blackdown mill undergoing repairs in 1979.
Photo: MLF

The smock mill, known as Cherry Clack mill, was changed over to steam power in the 1920s. One of its sweeps was sold for thirty shillings, the other three broken up for firewood.

Archie continued to grind oats for poultry feed on it until 1947 when he had to decide whether to let it rot away or pull it down. He chose a third option – to restore it, not as a tourist attraction but as a working mill. He had done a lot of remedial work on it by 1951 when the tower was struck by lightning and part of it burned away.

In 1979, five years after he had fitted the last pair of new sweeps and had the millstones turning again, there was another lighting strike. A lesser man would have given up but not Archie. He set about repairing the damage done by the storm to the new sweeps and by 1998 the mill was once again in working order.

There was also a smock mill which had been brought to Punnetts Town from Horeham Road in 1866 to operate the wood saw that had been installed in Blackdown mill but was interfering with the corn grinding process. The sweeps of the little smock mill worked a circular wood saw until a few years after the First World War. It was dismantled in 1927 and a bungalow built on the site.

Another mill to give way to the demands of the property market in the 1930s was the post mill at Sandy Cross – and it did so in style. 'Somebody wanted its old oak timbers to use in the building of a modern mansion,' said Arthur Beckett in his *Adventures of a Quiet Man*. 'Its externals were removed, its timbers sawn through, ropes and chains were attached and, with the assistance of many willing helpers from among the large crowd of onlookers, the mill was pulled over with a great crash' Its demise was commemorated in a poem by Thomas Hobden which includes these verses:

> One hundred years and more I've stood
> 'Midst rain and awful gales,
> And many a thunderstorm has passed
> With lightning round my sails.
>
> From Perasey Bay to Southdown heights
> My vision ever ran,
> But now I'm slumb'ring with the slain,
> Thrown to the ground by man.
>
> The miller shakes his bended head,
> Gazing upon the dust,
> While thoughts fly back to bygone days,
> And hates the Vandal's lust.

So now, my friend, I say adieu,
Your thoughts are saddened still;
For I am gone from off my stand,
Good-bye. SANDY CROSS MILL.

The Grade II listed Mill House at Sandy Cross was for sale in December 1998. It was described as occupying an elevated position 'commanding superb southerly views over open countryside' and included with it was 'the detached former mill building'.

Quite by chance Maurice Lawson Finch, when on holiday in Sussex in 1981, found a mill site he believed to be one marked on a map of 1575. He was driving from Flimwell to Angmering with his wife, Eileen, and stopped at Heathfield for a sandwich.

'I turned up the left fork at a parking sign into a small; but very clean car park. I got out of the car and found it was off Mill Road. I then walked up the road only a few yards and saw a house called Millcroft, the occupants of which were just leaving . . .'

As a result of this chance encounter Maurice learned that Millcroft was once the site of a mill cottage owned, with its adjoining land, in 1886 by Albert Fuller, a less rich relation of that famous Sussex eccentric, 'Mad Jack' Fuller, Member of Parliament, ironmaster, builder of follies and champion of lost causes.

❐ ❐ ❐

Hellingly

There is a mill site here of which there was only the most minimal record until Maurice Lawson Finch visited the village with Gilbert Catt, whose father and grandfather had worked Hamlin's mill at Hailsham, in search of further information about North Street mill.

Sunday 25 May 1980 was their lucky day. Maurice chanced upon copies of *Hellingly in the Old Days* by Charles and Ernest Pitcher for sale in the church. He bought one and found it mentioned Dicker mill, North Street mill and Grove Hill mill which 'stood opposite Cinderford Lane'.

'This is the one and only reference that I have so far found to Grove Hill mill', he said in his research notes. 'Unless under another name and parish this mill does not seem to have been recorded by H E S Simmons nor is it

An aerial view of Mill House taken in the late 1970s. It shows, to the east of the house, a circle marking the mill site with the old track running back from it to the road.

Gilbert Catt beside the millstone at Longbarn. Photo: MLF

mentioned in a single publication so far concerned with windmills.'

The mill-hunters found a French burr millstone set into the ground before the front door of Mill House at the top of Grove Hill, and at the side door there was a small 3ft diameter Derbyshire Peak stone. 'This stone was unusual in that it had very deep grooves cut into it the like of which I have not seen before', Maurice noted. They also came across another Derbyshire Peak millstone – a large one – acting as the base for a post bearing a nameplate at the entrance to a Longbarn in Grove Hill.

The site of North Street post mill (TQ 580150) is more in Horam than Hellingly. It is marked by a mound at the back of the garage at the bottom of the garden of Cherry Tree House. In his will of August 1729 the miller, William King, left instructions for it, and his house, to be sold and the proceeds divided equally between his children. The mill was blown down sometime after 1900, the date the site last appeared on a map.

Herstmonceux

A dispute between neighbours resulted in the Grade II listed post mill on the north side of the A271 at Herstmonceux (TQ 648122) having two roundhouses, one on top of the other. The story is perhaps apocryphal because it has no names or dates, and is told in a letter to *Country Life* in 1941 signed 'Grist'. It seems that after a quarrel with the miller his neighbour swore that he would stop the wind turning the sails of the mill. This he did by planting a line of trees to the southwest but when they grew to a height to have any effect on the sweeps the miller simply raised his windmill by adding another roundhouse.

The mill, which was built *c*1814, was standing derelict from the 1930s until it was bought in 1973 by a baker from Hailsham who had plans to restore it. However, these plans came to nothing and the mill was subject to a Dangerous Structure Notice when it was sold at auction, with the adjoining old bakery, at Hove Town Hall on 1 December 1993. The buyer was Dr Paul Frost, a Brighton

The two roundhouses of Windmill Hill mill.

University department head, who had lived in the Mill House next door for six years. The mill has been made safe and weatherproof and the Windmill Hill Windmill Trust formed to raise money for its full restoration.

When the new owner of a post mill about a mile to the east along the A271 at Bodle Street Green (TQ 651144) said in 1930 that he intended to pull it down because no tenant could be found for it the Society for the Protection of Ancient Buildings appealed to the public for contributions towards its preservation. Apparently without success, for on a fine Tuesday in March 1935 its sweeps were removed, a rope attached from the top of the structure to a traction engine belonging to the owners of the site,

Bodle Street mill on a card posted in August 1932.

agricultural engineers, J Barnes and Co., and 'with only slight pull by the engine the mill came down with a tremendous crash', reported the *Sussex Express*.

It had been built *c*1835 by a miller named Smith who had a watermill at Buxted and needed to increase his output. Its last miller was William King who went there as an apprentice in 1896 and stayed until grinding ceased in 1924 and the mill and the land it stood on sold to Barnes and Company.

◻ ◻ ◻

Icklesham

Hog Hill post mill's image has been spread around the world. It was the inspiration for the design logo adopted in the 1960s by farmer Dick Merricks for the boxes of Sussex apples he sent to Spitalfield and Covent Garden markets and planned to sell abroad when Britain joined the Common Market.

In the 1980s the mill reached even starrier heights – it was used by the former Beatle, Paul McCartney, now Sir Paul, as a recording studio.

The mill's future was in doubt after the Second World War. For a time it looked as if it would go the way of so many others but the miller's house and associated buildings were converted into a luxurious country house with the restored post mill, complete with mock sails, as an item of interest.

Paul McCartney and his wife, Linda, bought the property as a country home in 1984. They sought and received

Hog Hill post mill undergoing a change-of-use conversion. Photo:MLF

planning permission to convert the mill into a recording studio and the work was in progress when Maurice Lawson Finch visited the mill on 18 July 1984.

Iford

What may well be the first reference to a windmill in this country places it in this small village that lies to the east of the Lewes to Newhaven road. The *Testa de Nevill* in the manorial records of the Hundred of Swanborough has this entry:

1155
Hugo de Plaiz gave to the monks of Lewes the windmill in his manor of Iford, for the health of the soul of his father, 'qui jacet on capella de Lewes'.

The manor of Iford belonged after the Conquest to William de Warenne. It came with the lordship of the Rape of Lewes, the Conqueror's gift to one of his staunchest supporters. A likely site for the mill would be Iford Hill, 140ft above sea level.

Jevington

The windmill that stood 665ft above sea level on top of Willingdon Hill was confusingly called both Jevington mill and Willingdon mill – the confusion arising because Polegate windmill was also called Willingdon mill as it was in that parish until the boundaries were changed in 1939. The mill site is shown on maps from 1595 to 1813 and a marriage licence of 6 May 1639 bears the name 'John Gallad, miller of Jevington'.

In its account of the 'terrible storm of 6 February 1769' the *Sussex Weekly Advertiser* said that 'the door and windows of Willingdon mill were carried a great distance away' and in 1787 a band of smugglers was apprehended by three revenue men and seven Light Dragoons 'near the windmill on Jevington Hill'. Three years later Nicholas Chapman of Jevington was advertising for 'a good grinder for Willingdon mill' and in 1803 'Jevington Windmill' was one of the fourteen beacon sites set up in the county during the Napoleonic wars.

In 1929 the Reverend Walter Budgen found 'the stance of Willingdon mill consisting of the usual shallow circular depression, with some evidence of the position of the cross timbers and the remains of the masonry of the structure that enclosed the base'. In May 1980 Maurice Lawson Finch, accompanied by Uncle Herbert, went to inspect the site: :

> We located the spot quite accurately to the south of the Ordnance Survey triangulation stone but, try as we might, we could find no trace of a broken millstone reputed to lie in the turf . . . On the way up we met a white-haired old gentleman just leaving the summit on his way down to Jevington. We asked him about the windmill of which he had never heard but we spent a little while in discussion during which he pointed out a number of vantage points with a heavily silver-covered walking stick. It was Lord George Brown . . .

George Brown, MP for Belper, was Foreign Secretary in 1966 when Harold Wilson's government decided to apply for membership of the EEC. He lost his seat in the 1970 election, was created a life peer and lived in Willingdon Lane, Jevington until his death in 1985.

Six Swift Windmill (only one of its kind in England.)

Kingston

Ashcombe mill, the six sweep white-painted postmill that stood on Kingston Hill (TQ 392089) was blown down in what became known as the 'great March blizzard' of 1916. It had been built at a cost of £1,000 for miller John Weston in 1826-27 and was one of the very few six-sweep mills in the county.

But it was certainly not the only one of its kind in England, a claim made for it on one of a 'beautiful series of Fine Art Cards', pictured above, supplied free with three of Shurey Publications' titles, *Smart Novels, Yes or No* and *Dainty Novels.*

Lewes

The windmill that stood opposite St Anne's church, on a site now behind the Black Horse Inn, provided a temporary refuge for King Henry III's brother on 14 May 1264. Richard, Duke of Cornwall, King of the Romans, was being pursued by Simon de Montfort's victorious forces from the field of battle on the Race Hill. He and some of his followers ran into the mill, barred the door and held the pursuers at bay for a time before surrendering to Sir John Bevis.

The bases of three mills, now part of private houses, are all that is left today of those that stood on the hills in and around this county town and are described in detail by mill archivist, H E S Simmons, in the *Sussex County Magazine* of November 1941.

Two of the surviving bases belong to the Town Mill that was built in 1802 on a piece of ground by the old town wall to the west of St Michael's church (TQ 413101) to meet the demand for a public mill where corn could be ground for the inhabitants at a moderate price. This mill was bought some ten years later by corn merchant Samuel Smart and he moved it in 1819 to the foot of the Race Hill, (TQ 403101) leaving behind its flint and brick octagonal base, now known as the Round House in Pipe Passage.

The Round House, as a house, was bought on impulse by Virginia Woolf in 1919, but she and Leonard did not complete the purchase.

The Round House in Pipe Passage.

55

Instead they bought Monk's House at Rodmell when it came up for sale by auction in July that year.

The base of Smart's mill in 1992 when it was Windmill Lodge training yard in Spital Road

The smock mill's superstructure was mounted on a single storey base on its new site but had to be heightened by 20ft when the buildings of the new prison shielded it from the prevailing wind.

The mill was idle from 1899, its sweeps and fan removed in 1912 and the rest, except for the base, demolished ten years later. Before it became part of the Windmill Lodge racing stables complex this base was used as a garage and store and today – painted an eye-catching pink – it is a private house.

There was a mill in the vicinity of Spital Road which had more than its fair share of disasters before it burnt down in June 1887. The grinder, William Jenner, was killed when it was struck by lightning in August 1783 and three other men, sheltering there from the storm, were injured. Fourteen years later, when the post and trestle mill was working in a near gale force wind, a millstone broke and, said the *Sussex Weekly Advertiser,* 'forced divers pieces with great violence about the mill'. Luckily the miller had just left. Not so lucky was the girl who was hit on the head and seriously injured by one of the sweeps as she was leaving the mill on 2 March 1799. It may be from that unfortunate mill that the Windmill Inn in Spital Road, now a private house, took its name.

It was from another mill with a high accident rating that the third surviving roundhouse originated. Malling post mill, on the top of Malling Hill (TQ 422112) above the road to Ringmer, caused the death of a woman with its sweeps; fractured the skull of a grinder hoisting sacks by dropping tackle on him; and drew his brother into its machinery and broke his arm. Only in one of the accidents did the mill come off worst. In 1804 a sweep

The mill with many names. Photo: G A Catt collection.

broke off when it hit, but did not hurt, a cow grazing beneath it.

The mill burnt down in 1908 and its Sussex flint roundhouse was heightened, roofed with slates and became a pretty single storey private house with a well stocked garden. It is still in Mill Road today, screened from passing view by trees and hedges.

The white post mill that stood on a site off Juggs Lane (TQ 402093) that appeared on maps from 1724 to 1902 had various names – Southern mill, Payne's mill, Southover mill, White mill, Kingston mill – and it either fell in the storm of 1888 or was demolished about twelve months before the First World War and the bricks and foundations of its roundhouse later became part of a swimming pool. The postcard above confirms the later date. The photographer was James Cheetham, clerk and assistant schoolmaster at Lewes Prison until he retired in 1917. It is captioned in his handwriting and is stamped CHEETHAM-LEWES.

Mark Cross tower mill after the fire and, right, with its new turreted top.

Mark Cross tower mill as a private house in 1983. Photo: MLF

✗ M ✗

Mark Cross

The white painted tower mill that stood to the east of the A267 (TQ584316) was built in 1845 for Catharine Ashby, a farmer of Rotherfield, and was operated for many years by J Walters and Sons, an old Mark Cross family. The interior and the top of the mill tower was badly damaged by a fire on 26 July 1911 but it was given a new turretted top section and, without its sweeps and driven by steam power, its millstones continued to grind the Wealden farmers' corn until the Second World War. From the 1960s it was used as a private house and in 1982, when it had been extensively modernised, it was put on the market as a five bedroomed property with three quarters of an acre of land for between £80,000 and £85,000.

❏ ❏ ❏

Mayfield

Across the valley from Mark Cross, about one mile east of the church near which St Dunstan had his legendary encounter with the Devil, is Argos Hill post mill (TQ571283). It was built in 1835, ceased working in 1929 when its fan was blown off, and had lost its sweeps and its good looks by 1955 when its then owner offered it to Uckfield Rural District Council together with a strip of land round it and access to the site. The offer was accepted, East Sussex County

Argos Hill mill when it was working in 1920.

59

Council agreeing to pay half the cost of restoring and maintaining the mill. In 1976 it changed its mind and Wealden District Council ratepayers have picked up the tab ever since.

An earlier effort to save the mill had been made by Mr J Brook of Tooting who, in a letter published in the December 1931 issue of the *Sussex County Magazine,* described himself as 'an old windmiller' and asked to be 'put in touch with someone with a little capital' so he could keep going 'one at my native home which is in good repair inside and out'.

'I should use her for grinding fowl and pig corn. Sussex ground oats I should specialise in. . . It seems to me a shame that this mill should stand idle for want of a little capital when there is such a glorious opportunity to keep her going. She lies between Mayfield and Rotherfield and is called Argos Mill'. Mr Brook then resorted to verse:

THE OLD MILL

Proudly, boldly facing the storm,
For many a year she's stood,
And taken all weathers in right good form,
As only a windmill could.
For her heart is of stoutest British oak,
And all her timbers are good.

A pleasanter sight on a summer's day
I guess you have rarely found,
Than to see her dreamily grinding away,
Then off with a dash and a bound.
While shadow and sun in the meadow at play
Mimic the sails going round.

And when old Winter is here again
The sky with clouds to blur,
What ho! for blizzard, storm and rain,
On with a swish and a whirr.
Her arms may bend but the storm is her friend,
It's the merriest time for her.

Ah, here's a lesson, good Brother Dust,
To us and to every one,
For battle the storm of life we must,
Till life's last sand is run.

Newhaven

The smock mill now at North Common, Chailey, restored and receiving visitors, spent twenty-one years at this busy port. It was at Harmonden, West Hoathly, when Newhaven miller John Bollen bought it in 1884 to replace his post mill that had burnt down. A year after it had been re-erected on high ground to the south-southwest of the church (TQ 437011) Bollen died and the mill and his business was bought by George Stone. The firm of Stone and Thrower moved to a steam operated flour mill near the Bridge Inn in the 1860s and sold the smock mill to the Beard family who had it moved, on steel rollers, over to Chailey.

As well as a visiting mill Newhaven had a rather odd miller. It was said of Master Coombs that he painted his mill horses so that he could go to market each week on a horse of a different colour. He was also obsessively a man of his word. He swore he would never go into his windmill again if a certain statement he had made proved untrue. It did, and he did not. He would sit for hours each day at the top of the steps but never passed through the mill door.

□ □ □

Ninfield

A white-painted post mill with a brickwork base stood proudly to the north of the A271 (TQ 701127) from about 1825 until it was demolished in 1937. It had been brought from Boreham Street, where it was built in 1809, and ground corn at Ninfield for about 100 years before its last miller, William Morris, died.

To the south, at Lunsford's Cross on the

The three storey tarred brick base of Lunsford Cross smock mill now forms part of a private house. Photo: MLF 1988

west side of the A269 was Thorne smock mill (TQ 714109) which ceased working about 1905. When Maurice Lawson Finch visited the mill, which had been converted to a private house, he was told by the occupant that it had replaced a post mill that had been brought from Bexhill.

❒ ❒ ❒

Northiam

The two post mills that stood as a pair about a mile southwest of the church on a site (TQ 822232) and shown on maps from 1724 to 1825, no doubt gave the locality its name of Mill Corner. One was blown down, the other pulled down. There was no interest in Northiam High Park mill (TQ 823252) when it came up for auction at Rye in July 1937 and it was withdrawn and subsequently demolished.

❒ ❒ ❒

Nutley

One of the last five open trestle post mills in the country stands beside the Crowborough road (TQ 451291) at the north end of this village on the edge of Ashdown Forest. It came there in 1840, either from Crowborough or Goudhurst, and is thought to date from the late seventeenth century. The mill stopped working in 1905 and would have decayed away or been demolished had not a group of enthusiasts come to the rescue and formed the Uckfield and District Preservation Society in 1968. Four years later the mill's body was safely back on its single post and in June 1981, at the cost of less than £3,000, it ground its first hundredweight of corn.

Nutley's open trestle windmill at work again.
Photo: MLF 1980

Ore

The dramatic demise of the White mill that had stood to the north of the Ridge (TQ 835117) from *c*1813 until 16 May 1900 was described by an eye-witness in the *Hastings and St Leonards Chronicle* which also, in its issue of 19 May that year, announced the relief of Mafeking.

> When I first arrived on the scene dense clouds of smoke and a little flame were issuing from out of the top of the structure . . . The glass was shattered in the little windows and then the draught was increased. The roar of the fire grew louder and louder and the heat became more and more unbearable, steadily driving the crowd backward. The doors soon opened and then the scene was a splendid one, the interior of the mill could be seen to be a veritable furnace, nothing but a mass of flame was visible.
>
> The flames crept up and caught the sails, and then the end approached. The whole was almost completely enveloped in a wild mantle of fire. The heat thrown out was tremendous, and at times the black smoke was overpowering. . . Then crash! down came the whole concern. It did not sway at all, but gave one the impression of a huge concertina being compressed. At the moment of the fall a 'heatwave' of fearful power was caused and everyone was compelled to retire in haste, covering his face. The adjoining buildings, which had also been steadily burning and which were well tarred, collapsed. The lower part of the mill, of brick, was a seething furnace and the machinery was white hot. Rats and mice crawled about and ran hither and thither in their flight.

The miller was Isaac Cheale and that morning he had moved forty or more sacks of wheat into the mill, which luckily was insured.

Ore's Black mill, sited further to the east (TQ 839117) was built *c*1854 by two brothers, John and Joshua Thomas, who had learned the trade as apprentices at the White mill. However, after a few years they had to give up milling as the inhalation of dust had affected their lungs.

The smock mill was pulled down in 1920 and the base roofed over and converted to an artist's studio.

Peasmarsh

The smock mill in Mill Lane (TQ 880232) ceased working in 1920 and was quietly decaying away when it was bought ten years later by actress Sybil Arundale after it had failed to attract any reasonable bids and had been withdrawn by its owner, Mr C J Banister, from an auction sale at Rye. She said that she intended to have it converted to a house for her own occupation.

' Peasmarsh, The Mill Lane' is the caption on this undated postcard.

Playden

The condition of this post mill in August 1939 was described on the back of a postcard bearing a picture captioned THE OLD MILL AT RYE. It was then standing in the garden of a house in Mill Road (TQ 921214) which branches to the east off the A268.

The unknown researcher occupied all the space on the back of the card with these notes:

> This post mill appears to date from about 1730-40 though the sweeps may be 100 years later. The brick roundhouse is tarred black as is the body of the mill and steps. This mill has been sheeted over all but the back and the sheeting painted white. Roundhouse, one floor; mill two; and one in the head. Centre post from a large tree, the lower part in the roundhouse had the bark only shaved off. In mill itself the trunk has been rounded. No date on it anywhere . . . the wooden wheels still in the mill head also one stone left in position on first floor . . . the tailpole is broken off flush with steps. The cross tree is not much above ground left.
>
> 20th August 1930

The cap was removed from Polegate mill in 1987 and revealed corrosion in the metal runner underneath which had to be replaced at a cost of £3,000.

Photo: Sussex Express

Polegate

There is plenty that is special about the red brick tower mill that was built in 1817 on farmland to the west of the main London to Eastbourne Road. It was, said H E S Simmons in his comprehensive survey of Sussex mills, the only one to carry a five-bladed fan. The usual number is six or eight.

It is also a mill that has changed its location without being moved. When it was built to replace the old post mill that was forced out of its foundations and pieces of it scattered in all directions in a violent storm on 3 March 1817 it stood in Willingdon parish. However, boundary changes in 1939 brought the site in Park Croft (TQ 582041) into Polegate parish.

The mill was owned and worked by members of the Seymour family until the mid-nineteenth century when it was bought for £1,130 by farmer, coal merchant and licensee of the Red Lion, Willingdon, Matthias Mockett. The Red Lion in those days was a half-timbered house with a mangle room attached where the village washerwomen could wring out their clothes at the cost of a penny a bundle. It was later replaced by the hostelry frequented by Mr Jones, the farmer in Eric Blair's political fable *Animal Farm*, first published in 1945. When he was at the bar Farmer Jones 'would complain to anyone who would listen about the monstrous injustices he had suffered in being turned out of his own property by a pack of good-for-nothing animals . . .'

In 1918 Ephraim Ovenden bought the mill and worked it by wind until 1943 when the staging of the five-bladed fan needed replacing. He could not get the wood to repair it because it was wartime so he installed an electric motor and continued producing wholemeal flour until 1964 when he sold the mill for £1,000 to Eastbourne and District Preservation Trust which at once set about raising the money to renovate it. New sweeps were made by E Hole and Son of Burgess Hill and Polegate's tower mill was officially opened to the public by the Duke of Devonshire in 1967.

Twenty years later, after concentrated money-raising, £20,000 worth of restoration work was put in hand. The sweeps were renewed and the cap lowered to the ground, renovated and replaced with a new fantail in position. By 1989 the sweeps were turning again and, in the mill and its adjoining buildings, a museum of milling was set up.

The post of Ringmer smock mill. Photo MLF 1986

Ringmer

There was conflict about the date and cause of the collapse of the post mill that stood to the north of the Ringmer to Glynde road (TQ 450112). According to some published reports it was blown over in a gale either in the winter of 1924 or the summer of 1925 but the record is put straight by Henry Martin, whose forebears owned the mill and who was instrumental in getting its post restored. In a letter to the *Sussex Daily News* of 8 November 1938 he says:

> The actual date was Saturday, 6 June 1925 and I have a photo of the wreckage taken an hour afterwards. It was a perfectly calm afternoon but recent winds had torn at the structure. At the time a mother was picnicking with two children and she said: 'Come away, I don't like the look of that old mill'. The children had scarcely joined her when the mill collapsed. The noise of the crash was heard for a couple of miles around and hundreds of people flocked to the spot for relics.

When faced with a disaster to a windmill people tend to rush into verse. These lines entitled *The Passing of Ringmer Mill* and dated 7 June 1925, handwritten on pale blue writing paper with here and there some crossings out and corrections, were in Maurice Lawson Finch's Ringmer file, but with no clue as to the identity of their author.

> Down with a crash! upon the distant hill
> Ere sunshine fades, and daylight gently dies
> There in this summer day, the ancient mill
> With long unnumbered years – a ruin lies.
>
> The moonbeams creep along the shattered floor,
> Amid the rafters shadows pale are cast,
> Midst haunting memories of days of yore
> The poor old mill has bowed its head at last.
>
> A tangled heap, the pride of bygone years
> I stand and gaze in wonder fraught with pain
> Oh ! I am sad, but must withhold my tears
> The Knell of Death proclaims regrets are vain.
>
> Some hands will come and quickly bear away
> Each fragment there, with history written deep.
> Then – a lone spot – on each encroaching day,
> Upon that cherished ground the weeds will creep.
>
> Long years will pass and children yet unborn,
> With infant feet will wander on that hill.
> And friends, perchance, another summer morn
> Full carelessly will say – here stood Ringmer Mill.

The smock mill ground corn until 1921. All that now remains above ground is the original post, with replacement supporting beams added in 1968 when, as a cast iron plaque states, it was re-erected by Glyndebourne Estate Trust 'to restore a well known local landmark'.

> *Tempora qua prisco Zephyyris*
> *Mea vela volabant*
> *Praeteritim postis ian notat*
> *Ipse Decus.*

Ringmer also had a mill on the south side of The Broyle. It burnt down in 1905.

Rodmell

Three sepia postcards showing an identical picture of a post mill with the Downs to the east of the Ouse in the background and a man ploughing with a pair of horses in the foreground, have different captions.

On one, postmarked 6 August 1912, is: AN OLD SUSSEX WINDMILL.

On another, postmarked 27 August 1912, is: SOUTHEASE MILL, SUSSEX.

On a third, posted on 15 February 1927, is: OLD MILL, RODMELL.

There were two mill sites in this village which became a centre of literary interest when Leonard and Virginia Woolf moved into Monk's House in 1919. One shown on maps from 1753 to 1795 was on Mill Hill at the top of Mill Lane (TQ 412056). The other, the mill on the postcards, was on maps from 1813 until 1901. It was on the opposite side of Mill Lane, to the north of Rodmell Hill House (TQ 417057).

❏ ❏ ❏

Rottingdean

A mill was listed here in a commission report of 1548, and appears on a title deed in 1611. Thirty-five years later 'Rottingdean miller' Richard Aylwin, was before the justices in Lewes for assault.

Bazehill post mill at Rottingdean.

The mill in the title deed stood on the right of the Bazehill Droveway on the way up to High Barn (TQ 371030). This post mill probably formed part of the tithes of the church for the vestry notes of 1733 mention a mill tax. In 1795 a Mr Kennard is assessed at '£2 rent and five shillings tythes' for the mill, presumably in working order again after the storm of November 1773 when the *Sussex Weekly Advertiser* reported:

On Monday last, the wind blowing very hard at north east, did a great deal of damage in the country, particularly to the windmills; Rottingdean mill was drove to such fury that all efforts to stop it proved ineffectual till the swifts were torn from the round and beam, which proved a lucky circumstance, as 'tis that which prevented her taking fire.

The mill was for sale by auction in 1813 at the White Horse, Rottingdean and four years later it was advertised for sale again:

> To be sold to be removed a Post Windmill carrying two pairs of stones with all the necessary machinery complete and a good round house situate in the Parish of Rottingdean. Inquire of Stephen Henly, miller.

There is no later record of any actual removal but subsequent maps show only one mill – except for the revised Ordnance Survey of 1843, from which the old mill was not deleted.

The black smock mill on Beacon Hill was built for Thomas Beard in 1802. The date is to be found inside with 'T B' beside it. In his Letter Book, in 1825 Beard complains about the refusal of his bread by the men of the Coastal Blockade at Crowlink and Cuckmere Haven and insists that it is 'exceedingly fine, sweet and good.' He was not at all pleased to learn that they were

Restoration work in progress on Rottingdean's Beacon Hill mill in 1935-36

buying bread from Seaford 'by which I sustain an enormous loss'.

The mill did not figure in the 1910 inventory of the possessions of the last Beard of Rottingdean so by then it must have been sold out of the family. Some restoration work was done on it in 1935-36 and in October 1970 an appeal for £4,000 to save the mill was launched.

□ □ □

Tillingham mill, Rye, in 1910, when it was still working and, right, the replica erected in 1933 after the fire and, below, the replica in 1972, after its fibre glass facelift.

Rye

In his will dated February 1587 John Mercer of Rye left to his wife, Joane, his house in Middle Street and 'my newe windmill and lande thereto belonging and also my three parts of the other windmill next adjoining thereto'. These two mills could have been the ones shown on the map drawn up from a pre-Armada survey of the county and published by Mark Anthony Lower in 1870. They stood on Rye Hill, by the road to Playden, a site now on Mill Road to the east of the A268.

Another pair of mills appear on later maps to the north of the road to Udimore, on either side of what is now Tillingham Lane. They had a variety of names – Strand mill, Barry's mill, Wilkinson's mill, Chatterton's mill – but the 140ft high smock mill on the site (TQ 916204) that burnt down in 1930 was known as Tillingham Mill. The fire started in Albert Webb's bakehouse which adjoined the mill that he rented from Rye Corporation on condition that he kept it in a reasonable state of preservation. Painters had been at work on the mill, which was undergoing extensive repairs, on the day the fire started – late in the evening of unlucky Friday 13 June.

'The structure was soon a column of seething flame that lit up the landscape like a beacon and was seen for miles around and far out to sea,' the *Sussex County Magazine* of September 1930 told its readers. 'The climax came when the cap of the mill, with the fantail and heavy gearing wheels, a blazing mass weighing several tons, crashed to the ground in a cataract of sparks. It was all over in a little over half an hour, and then all that remained of this picturesque veteran were its lower walls of gaping brickwork . . .'

The mill, built in 1820 – the date carved on one of its beams – ceased grinding corn in 1912 and had become an historic landmark, much painted and photographed by Rye's artist community and visitors to the Cinque Port. It was so much missed that a replica was constructed in 1933 and given a £1,200 glass fibre facelift some thirty years later. In 1984 it opened as the Windmill Guest House and has been in the ownership of Bob and Pauline Adams from 1999.

Seaford

A house was brought by barge down the Ouse from near Lewes and re-built on a site near Seaford Head, occupied before 1783 by a fortified mill. The story of Corsica Hall's removal, brick by brick, from Wellingham to Millberg at the instigation of watchmaker-turned-banker, Thomas Harben, has been told many times. Another often-told tale is the tragic one recorded in Seaford's parish register for 24 February 1773:

Sutton mill c1900.

Buried, James, son of Joseph and Elizabeth Stevens, killed by a sweep of Mr Washer's windmill.

This accident occurred at Sutton post mill, built in 1769 for Thomas Washer at Two Acres (TQ 488994) now Mill Drive and Milldown Road. His family, it is said, also owned the Millberg mill and the Black mill at West Blatchington. Sutton mill was demolished in 1904 but the millhouse still stands at the eastern corner of Sutton Road's junction with the A259.

Less well known is the information imparted by Thomas Burton, born in Seaford *c*1898, in a letter to his brother-in-law, H R Briggs, concerning the fantail of 'that windmill that Tommy Funnell had over his workshop'. He goes on:

Now here is something for you to think about – did it come from Sutton mill or

74

did it come from the mill at Ringmer. He did have something to do with that mill. The bottom or round houses they call them he brought to Seaford to put in his garden, the lower part he used as workshop and garage and the upper part as a summer house. He brought this from Ringmer on the trailer of his traction engine. All this he told me when May and I went in his house and had tea once . . . He told me himself people at Ringmer and at Seaford said he would never get it to Seaford because of the bridges he would have to pass, but he found a way round the countryside and made it. The name of Tommy Funnell's house was Green Woodpecker because he had green glazed tiles on the roof and white walls to the house, first house on the left up Kammond Road.

In April 1985 Maurice Lawson Finch called at Green Woodpecker and was shown the orginal drawings of the house Funnell had built. They were stamped 'planning approval 12 Dec 1938'. In the next door garden, for the site had been split up in the 1960s, was the circular base of the roundhouse.

The Black mill on Bullock Down dated from Tudor times and its replacement, a pumping mill, was surrounded from 1897 by the new golf course laid out by J H Taylor until it, too, was demolished.

❐ ❐ ❐

The pumping mill on Bullock Down.

Staplecross

Villagers here did not have to go far for their flour or their beer before the First World War as a smock mill, built in 1815, and a brewery stood side by side about 100 yards or so behind the post office and a row of shops.

The mill ceased working in the 1920s and served as a Home Guard post during the Second World War when it narrowly missed being destroyed as

The smock mill and old brewery at Staplecross on a card posted in 1905.

Luftwaffe pilots jettisoned their bombs on their way back across the Channel pursued by the Spitfires and Hurricanes of the Royal Air Force.

By 1950, when the villagers tried to get the mill preserved, it had lost the shutters of its sweeps and some of the rails of its staging. Ewhurst parish council approached the Society for the Protection of Ancient Buildings in the hope of getting it repaired but without success and it was taken down and the base is now part of a private house.

❏ ❏ ❏

Stone Cross

A £142,000 lottery grant plus funds raised from other sources have made it possible for the Stone Cross Windmill Trust to get the white tower mill in Beggar's Lane, Rattle Road (TQ619044) back in full working order. This pretty mill with its porthole windows was built in 1876-77 for Samuel Dallaway and worked until 1937 with Samuel's son, Harry, as the miller. It has an unusually large diameter base which served as a store, loading stage and as a deck from which the four double-shuttered patent sweeps could be reached for adjustment and maintenance. It lost a pair of these sweeps in a gale in 1928 and carried on working with two. Seven years later the cover of Eastbourne's Parsonage Mill, which had been trundled to the site on a trolley by Samuel Dallaway to serve as a grain store at Stone Cross, was demolished.

There was talk of the mill becoming a museum in the 1980s and temporary planning permission was granted for this use. In 1993 the owner, Simon Hall, whose father had spent years doing restoration work on the tower mill, handed it over to Wealden District Council so it could be preserved and his late father's wishes for it to be open to the public fulfilled. And they were from 2002. The millstones are now grinding again and every summer Sunday it is open to visitors from 2-5pm.

Stone Cross mill tucked neatly behind the new houses of Windmill Close. Eileen and Simeon are in the foreground. Photo: MLF 1974

◻ ◻ ◻

The post mill in the village of Udimore before it was pulled down in 1922.

Udimore

This mill, which had a copper coin dated 1790 attached to its main post, replaced one that occupied the site (TQ 869190) from 1694. It had been built for miller and farmer, John Sloman, who lived in the nearby Vines Farmhouse which remained in his family until the nineteenth century. In a letter to the *Sussex County Magazine* of October 1930 Edmund Austin said that the present Mill House was built by Peter Stonham, a relative of the Slomans, in 1817 and he carried on the milling business until 1856 when he was succeeded by John Collins Henley. He died in 1868 and his brother Henry Henley took over the mill and remained there until his death in 1921 at the age of eighty-eight.

The mill was demolished in 1922 and a quantity of its timber used in the restoration of some old houses in Church Square, Rye. A more dramatic account of its last days is given by A C Bradley in *An Old Gate of England,* published in 1918:

The conspicuous note of Udimore is, or rather was, its windmill. Perched high above the road at the topmost point of the village, when its sails were whirling and groaning in a high wind against a wild sky, one trembled in passing for the people of Udimore who lay upon the leeward side, for with such a precarious grip did the quivering body of the huge mill seem to cling to its exalted perch.

The last time I passed this way I found that the sails had gone, and sought information of the village oracle.

'Yes, sir, the mill has stopped work', he said.

'How is that?' said I.

'Well, sir, people had begun to think it was not safe.'

I should think they had.

So another ancient windmill and a far-reaching landmark has vanished. It will not, I fear, be pensioned off in the interests of the picturesque like that of Winchelsea when it went out of business a few years ago.

This romantic country scene is on a card posted on 17 August 190–, entitled 'THE PATH TO THE MILL, WADHURST'

The roundhouse of Riseden mill in 1973, with the fallen main post protruding from it.
Photo: MLF

Wadhurst

The post mill at Riverhall may well have been the model for the painting on the postcard, pictured left, for Maurice Lawson Finch has this note in his file:

On Rother mill stream
FOR SALE JUNE 1983
MILL HOUSE, RIVERHALL
WADHURST

He has no further information on this mill but plenty on Riseden post mill, shown on maps from 1823 on a site south of Riseden Road (TQ 621303). It collapsed on a still day in 1910 and its roundhouse with the mill's fallen main post protruding from it was a feature of the garden of Windmill Cottage, Riseden Road, when Mr R Overton was living there. He had pulled the centre post down with the aid of a rope and a windlass in 1973 and set the top of it in a square flag-stoned flower bed in the lawn behind his house. And he had placed three of the millstones within the paving of the patio.

There is little surviving physical evidence of other mills around Wadhurst. The post mill that stood behind the Mill House, Cousley Wood which faces the B2100 Wadhurst to Lamberhurst road, was in a dilapidated state in 1885 and has now totally disappeared. Standen's mill, shown on Bestbeech Hill in 1795 and White's mill, shown near Butcher's Wood, on maps from 1866-1894, have also vanished without trace.

◻ ◻ ◻

Waldron

Quite by chance, in May 1981 when he was driving from Flimwell to Angmering with his wife, Eileen, Maurice Lawson Finch found the site (TQ 578 212) of a post mill believed to be the one marked on a map of 1575. They had stopped in Heathfield for a sandwich at about 4.30pm,

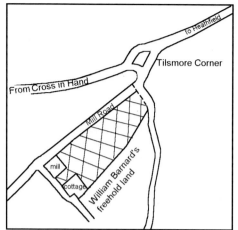

Copy of a site map dated 4.11.1885. The hatched area was bought by Bertram Watson in 1914.

'having not eaten since 10am that morning', and parked 'in a small but very clean car park off Mill Road'.

Maurice got out of the car and walked up the road only a few yards and saw a house called Millcroft, the owners of which were just leaving. What he learned from a subsequent exchange of letters with Mrs Mary Evans of Millcroft was that the mill cottage had belonged in 1886 to Albert Fuller, a distant and not-so-rich relative of Sussex eccentric 'Mad Jack' Fuller, Member of Parliament, builder of follies, ironmaster and local philanthropist. The site was bought in 1914 by Heathfield estate agent, Bertram Watson, and later houses were built on it.

❏ ❏ ❏

Warbleton

Herbert Finch on the site of Summer Hill post mill.
Photo.: MLF 1979

The foundations of the piers of Summer Hill post mill could be clearly seen in a field to the west of the road from Chapel Cross to Chapman's Town (TQ 619192) when Maurice Lawson Finch, accompanied by his uncle, Herbert Finch, visited the

The roundhouse of Short's mill with its new roof. Photo: MLF 1979

site on 2 October 1979. The mill that was there from *c*1824 until it was pulled down in 1935 was operated by Ellis Brothers, millers of Warbleton.

On the same day, further to the south (TQ 616184) he also found and photographed the octagonal base of Short's mill which was also known as Chapman's Town Black mill. He noted that it was built of large blocks, tarred over on the outside obviously a long time ago, and fitted with a new octagonally-pointed green roof. There was a door opening on the side parallel to the road and a single window on the far side, the height of the structure being at a guess about 8ft to the roof.

❏ ❏ ❏

Wartling

On the same day, Maurice and his uncle made another discovery. On the east side of the A271 from Herstmonceux to Ninfield (TQ662166) they found a

83

Boreham Street mill on a card posted on 22 August 1917 and , below left, the millstone doorstep of the Lamb Inn.

grass mound, next to the premises of Boreham Mill Nurseries. It had a circular depression on the top where the main post of Boreham Street post mill would have been – a site shown on maps from 1813 to 1920. The mill was pulled down in 1926 but its last owner, a Mr Sinden, had not been forgotten. 'He was a wicked man who ran the mill on a Sunday,' the researchers were told by the owner of the site.

They had another find in Wartling on 27 May 1980. They stopped for lunch at the Lamb Inn, just off the A259 Pevensey Marsh road, and noticed that the step at the entrance, pictured left, was a millstone. 'Where' they wondered, 'did that come from' for they were on the Pevensey Levels and there were no mill sites in the near vicinity.

Westham

A post mill that was in regular use from *c*1724 until it was blown down in the storm of 14 October 1881, stood on Mill Hill to the north of Peelings Lane (TQ 630051). It was known as Crisford's or the Black mill, the last miller being Charles Crisford, and appeared on Admiralty charts as a navigation mark to be lined up with the tower of Westham church by ships passing up-Channel.

For some thirty years after its destruction navigators continued taking bearings on Westham church and a windmill, but they were lining up with Stone Cross mill instead, with the result that their vessels approached too near to the coast. It was not until 1924 that the Admiralty learned what had happened and altered its charts. How this occurred is recounted by E V Welby of Mill House, Westham, in a letter published in the *Sussex County Magazine* of December 1936:

Pieces of Derbyshire Peak millstones from Crisford's mill form part of a path in a rockery at Mill Hill Farm. Photo: MLF 1980

> A naval officer was taking bearings from the tower of Westham church and, after checking with the charts he had with him, pointed to Mill Hill and said to the vicar: 'This is curious. According to my chart there ought to be a windmill on that hill'
> 'There was but it was blown down in 1882', the vicar replied.

When England was under threat from Napoleon's armies massed across the Channel a mill at Westham was ordered to be fortified. But which one? It seemed reasonable to suppose, as H E S Simmons did, that it would have been a mill near to the sea and Pevensey mill, shown on the 1860-1874 OS

Westham's windpump at Singleton.
Photo MLF 1983

map some 220yards south west of Westham church, fitted the description. Maurice and Uncle Herbert searched the churchyard, the playing field of the school close by, and an area of rough ground to the west but to no avail.

They may well have passed the site of the strange wind machine that they came across some years later when they visited Singleton Open Air Museum in West Sussex. It was a hollow post pumping mill, built in the nineteenth century and used to drain the clay pits to the southeast of the railway station. Its four small sails drove an upright shaft which turned the two eccentric cams that drove the twin cast iron lifting pumps. The mill, which stood on an open trestle, was turned into the wind by a circular non-revolving wooden vane occcupying the fantail position at the top rear of the bodywork. It was removed from its original site in 1975.

❏ ❏ ❏

Wilmington

When investigating what he believed to be a round barrow on the northern edge of Wilmington Wood (TQ 573081) in 1945 Mr S Salvage discovered what appeared to be the site of a windmill. He visited it again some years later and found it occupied by a family of badgers. Their earth-moving activities had turned up a calcined Sussex brown flint – an indication that the mill burnt down – and a large piece of stone which, when examined, proved to be part of a French burr millstone.

It seems that he had found the site of the mill mentioned in the Court

Rolls for 1691. One of the first entries refers to:

> . . . half an acre of land on the South Common in Hailsham, with the windmill built thereon, late Stonestreets's, formerly Hyland and Reinolds and once Poole's.

It was in the hands of William Coombs of Seaford in 1711 after which it disappeared – burnt down, no doubt, hence the calcined flint – for in 1735 the land is described as 'half an acre of land on which a windmill formerly stood'. The site is today within woodland but those trees have had two and a half centuries to grow over it.

In 1393 there was a mill much nearer Wilmington, rather than on the edge of the parish's boundary with Hailsham. It is mentioned in an

The piece of French burr millstone dug up by badgers on the site in Wilmington Wood. Photo: MLF 1978

assessment of that date carried out by the prior of Michelham into the amount of waste and destruction that occurred when Sir Edward Dalyngridge was in possession of Wilmington priory and its lands. It had been granted to him by King Richard II in 1389 at an annual rent of £10 in lieu of the 100 marks a year owed to him for his services to the Crown and while he held it Sir Edward, like earlier lessees, made as much as he could out of it. Among the dilapidations listed in the assessment was 6s 8d worth of damage to 'the windmill and bridge at Munchenepende with the warren there . . .' The site (TQ 551058) is to the east of Thornwell Road where there is both Monkyn Pyn and Warren Farm marked on OS maps

❏ ❏ ❏

This undated postcard shows St Leonard's mill, Winchelsea, when it was still working.

The base of St Leonards mill, Winchelsea with one of the millstones displayed beside it after its last restoration by the National Trust.

Photos: MLF 1984

Winchelsea

In Lewes a windmill gave temporary refuge to the brother of King Henry III in 1264 but a windmill at Winchelsea nearly killed his son. King Edward I was ready to set sail for France in August 1297 and was at this Cinque Port for a final review of the fleet when the horse he was riding was frightened by the noise made by the sweeps of a mill and refused to pass it. The king urged the animal on with spurs and whip and it leapt over a wall and landed safely on the road below, sliding deep into the mud. Edward remained in the saddle, turned his mount round and rode back through the Strand Gate where the people waiting for him were 'filled with wonder and delight at his miraculous escape,' says Thomas of Walsingham in his account of the incident.

A plaque bearing the words:

ON THIS SITE STOOD ST LEONARD'S WINDMILL, DESTROYED
IN THE GREAT STORM OF THE 16TH OCTOBER 1987.
THE WINDMILL WAS BUILT IN 1703 ON THE SITE OF
THE ANCIENT SAXON CHURCH OF ST LEONARDS ON
WHICH YOU ARE NOW STANDING.

is all that remains of a post mill (TQ 902176) that was a prominent and frequently restored landmark in the locality. It stopped working around 1905 and the sweeps, windshaft and machinery were removed some years later. By 1935 it was in a derelict and dangerous condition and was restored as a result of local initiative. Some twenty years later it was derelict again and the then owner, Winchelsea's mayor, Anthony Freeman, offered to give it away with a cheque for £100, to anyone who was prepared to restore and maintain it.

There were no takers. East Sussex County Council declined the offer because it had received an adverse

The 'derelict and dangerous mill prior to its first restoration . Photo: SCM

report about the proposed restoration from the county architect. However, the mill was eventually restored by the National Trust, then owners of the land on which it stood.

In 1978 a framework of steel girders was built inside the structure and the cladding renewed. And that should have secured the future of St Leonard's mill for many years – but then came the hurricane force winds of the night of 16 October 1987 and blew it all down. The National Trust decided against re-building as so much in the way of new materials would be required that the final result would have been a reproduction rather than restored old mill.

The end of the much-restored mill at Winchelsea – and so many other Sussex windmills – brought about by the wind that drove their sweeps for centuries. Photo: MLF 1991

This poem, from the Dartford Young Farmers' Club's magazine of 1966, was the last item in Maurice's seventh box file.

THE WIND

The wind, a howling monster, which utters eerie cries as it
Encircles trees and whistles down the chimney,
Howling around the house like an angry warrior,
Knocking on the windows and creeping through the cracks.
Turning the dull green grass into a living mass of velvet,
Blowing tiles from roofs and leaves from the trees,
Whipping the calm glistening sea into a leaping fury,
Which lashes at the cliff walls and smashes little boats to pieces.

Streaking through the undergrowth of woods,
Sending the woodland creatures scattering,
Blowing people into the raging sea,
And chasing the scudding clouds across the sky.
A wet wind, driving rain before it,
And drenching everything and everyone,
A dry wind, blowing litter all over the place,
And bowling clanking dustbin lids merrily before it.
Until at last, running out of breath,
It becomes calm, and takes a look at the damage it has done,
And at the mess that lies in its wake.
Then it creeps shamefacedly away to hide itself.

MARGARET WEBB

Cruchley's 1858 map showing the sites, circled by MLF, of the mills in the Brighton and Lewes area of East Sussex.

APPENDIX 1

Maps on which East Sussex mill sites are shown

1579   Christopher Saxton's map of Sussex, Surrey, Kent and Middlesex
1587   A survey of the coast of Sussex made by two deputy lieutenants,
Sir Thomas Palmer and Sir William Covert, to see what parts
required additional sea defences against the threatened invasion
from Spain. It was published by Mark Anthony Lower in 1870
1610   John Speed's map of Sussex
1727   Richard Budgen's map of Sussex shows fifty mill sites
1795   Yeakell and Gardner. *The Great Survey* in four sheets
1813   This is the usually quoted date of the first Ordnance Survey map. A
total of six sheets, covering the entire county, were published
between 1810 and 1819 and they show 153 windmill sites
1825   Charles and John Greenwood's map of Susssex
1858   Cruchley's *Environs of Brighton*. See facing page

BIBLIOGRAPHY

Austen, Brian. *Windmills of Sussex*. Sabre Publishing 1978

Baines, J Manwaring. *Historic Hastings*. F J Parsons 1955

Batten, M I. *English Windmills*. Architectural Press 1930

Beckett, Arthur. *Adventures of a Quiet Man*. Combridges, Hove

Bennett, Richard and Elton, John. *History of Corn Milling*. Vols 1-4. Simpkin
     Marshall 1898-1904

Brangwyn, Frank and Preston, Hayter. *Windmills*. John Lane 1923

Brunnarius, Martin. *Windmills of Sussex*. Phillimore 1979

Budgen, Rev Walter. *Old Eastbourne, Its Church, Its Clergy, Its People*.1912

Gilbert, Edmund W. *Brighton, Old Ocean's Bauble*. Methuen 1954

Hemming, Rev Peter. *Windmills in Sussex*. C W Daniels and Company 1936

Hopkins, R Thurston. *Old English Mills and Inn*s. Cecil Palmer 1927
                   Old Watermills and Windmills. Phillip Allan 1931
                   Windmills. Charles Clarke, Haywards Heath

Long, George. *The Mills of Man*. Herbert Joseph 1931

Mais, S P B. *England of the Windmills*. Dent 1931

Martin, A Edward. *Life in a Sussex Windmill*. Allen and Donaldson 1920

Paddon, J P. *Windmills of East Sussex*. Oxonian Press

Powell G M and Hughes, A Foord. *Windmills in Sussex*. Walkers Galleries 1930

Simmons H E S. *Sussex Windmill Survey*.

Magazines.
Country Life
Sussex County Magazine
Sussex Life

Newspapers
Brighton Herald
Hastings Chronicle
Sussex Weekly Advertiser
Sussex Daily News
Sussex Express
Kent and Sussex Courier

ACKNOWLEDGEMENTS

In his files Maurice Lawson Finch listed those he wished to thank for their generous help and assistance in his windmill researches. In respect of East Sussex mill sites they were:

Mrs Mary Evans, Heathfield
A G Jakens, Seaford
Mrs Pat Berry, Seaford Museum
Mr and Mrs Harper, Hellingly
Lawrence Stevens, Eastbourne – 'I spent an evening with him on 20 Aug 1979' he noted.
S Salvage, Hailsham – 'He took H F Finch, myself and son Simeon to site of ancient mill in Wilmington Forest 8am 22 Aug 1970'.
Gilbert A Catt, Hailsham
Richard Gilbert, Eastbourne
Frank Gregory, Brighton

He also wished to thank the curator and staff of Hastings Museum and Art Gallery, the staff of the Eastbourne branch of the East Sussex County Library and of the East Sussex Record Office,

PICTURE CREDITS

Wherever the information is available pictures are individually credited. Many of the postcards give no details of the publisher and those from the late Gilbert Catt's collection of mill pictures, which he kindly made available to Maurice Lawson Finch, give no information about the copyright holder or publisher.